W9-AWB-603

Full-color Activity Pages

Fun Stuff Activity Book

GAME ON!

Based on the series created by Dan Povenmire & Jeff "Swampy" Marsh

Contributing Writer: Kathryn Knight

Contributing Artist: Scott Neely

Copyright © 2010 Disney Enterprises, Inc. All rights reserved.
Published by Dalmatian Press, LLC, in conjunction with
Disney Enterprises, Inc. www.disneychannel.com Printed in the U.S.A.

18598 Disney Phineas and Freb Fun Stuff Activity Book
10 11 12 NG 36029 9 8 7 6 5 4 3 2

All Answers are on pages 23 & 24

ROLLIN' INTO SUMMER

"So, Ferb, what do you wanna do today? I, for one, am starting to get bored, and boredom is something which I will not deal with! The first thing they're going to ask us when we get back to school is, 'What did you do over the summer?' I mean, no school for three months? Our lives should be a **rollercoaster**! And I mean a good rollercoaster, not like that one we rode at the state fair. That was lame."

PHINEAS'S BOREDOM-BUSTIN' BRAINSTORMIN'

Nothin' to do? Try filling in this chart using each letter in Phineas's name.

	Name of a city	Name of a country	A toy or game	A cool animal to have as a pet	Something you build
P					
H					
I					
N					
E					
A					
S					

FERB'S NOGGIN NUDGERS

How many total triangles can you find in this picture?

Hint: There are more than 12!

Fill in the numbers 1 to 9 so that each straight line of three numbers totals 18.

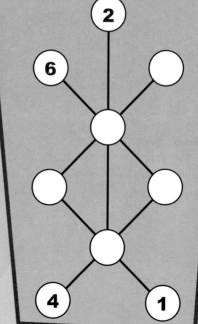

2

6

4   1

Here's something fun to do on a summer day: design and build your own rollercoaster!

We're going to need a blowtorch and some more peanut butter.

Phineas needs your help. Can you figure out which of these pieces complete the rollercoaster framework?

Phineas&
COOLEST CO
EVER

A   B   C

D   E   F

Solid-fuel booster rockets and snakes released during the corkscrew. Cool, huh?

There are 6 differences between these two pictures. Can you spot them It's a little challenging, so look very closely!

Phineas and Ferb have fixed up their mom's car to race in the Swamp Oil **500**! Can you lead them to the finish line?

START

FINISH

TEAM PHINEAS

You two are so busted!

4

1. What is Phineas's last name?

＿ ＿ □ ＿ ＿

2. What is Ferb's last name?

＿ □ ＿ ＿ ＿ ＿

3. Where did Phineas carve a replica of his sister's face? **MOUNT** ＿ □ ＿ ＿ ＿ ＿

4. What's a semi-aquatic egg laying mammal?

＿ ＿ ＿ □ ＿ ＿ ＿

5. Who is Dr. Doofenshmirtz's daughter?

＿ ＿ ＿ □ ＿ ＿ ＿

6. Phineas's rollercoaster takes them to where? **OUTER** □ ＿ ＿ ＿ ＿

7. What is Dr. Doofenshmirtz's first name?

＿ ＿ □ ＿ ＿

8. Phineas writes with what on his rollercoaster permit?

＿ ＿ □ ＿ ＿

9. There are 104 days of what vacation?

＿ ＿ ＿ □ ＿ ＿

PERRY the PLATYPUS

Phineas and Ferb have an unusual pet
named Perry. He's a platypus.
He doesn't do much.
(That's what Phineas and Ferb think!)

Are these statements about a platypus true or false?

	True	False
1. Lives a semi-aquatic life.	☐	☐
2. Breathes air.	☐	☐
3. Likes to dress up in a ball gown.	☐	☐
4. Has a spur on the hind ankle that delivers a venomous jab.	☐	☐
5. Hatches from an egg.	☐	☐
6. Has a rubbery duckbill snout.	☐	☐
7. Is native to South Africa.	☐	☐
8. Has a thick tail like a beaver.	☐	☐
9. Has webbed, clawed feet like an otter.	☐	☐
10. Enjoys playing mah-jong.	☐	☐
11. Prefers to stay hidden away in a burrow.	☐	☐
12. Emits low growls.	☐	☐

Never say a CROSS WORD to an animal!

Each word in the puzzle is a kind of animal.
Each word rhymes with its picture clue.
Can you complete the puzzle?

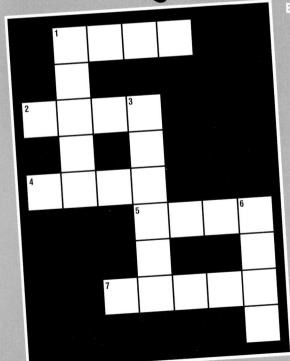

ACROSS

1 BOWL

2 TRUCK

4 BOOT

5 ROAD

7 RAKE

DOWN

1 HOUSE

3 MITTEN

6 EAR

Hey, Buford and Baljeet? Can you unscramble these letters to spell other types of unusual pets?

Uh...

I am able to.

UNSCRAMBLE

K U S N K
_ _ _ _ _

M A L L A
_ _ _ _ _

A N A I G U
_ _ _ _ _ _

D I P S E R
_ _ _ _ _ _

F R E E T R
_ _ _ _ _ _

R O O N C C A
_ _ _ _ _ _ _

Ferb pays attention to details—even when he's giving a monkey a shower.

Do you notice details? Study this picture below for 60 seconds. Then turn the page. How many questions can you correctly answer about this scene?

Monkey Shower

Did you study the scene on page 7
of Ferb giving a monkey a shower?
Got it engrained in your brain? Great!

1. What color is the shower curtain?_____
2. How many monkeys are in the tub?_____
3. What is hanging on the wall directly
   behind Ferb?_____
4. What kind of wood are the walls made of? _____
5. Is there water in the sink? _____
6. What is outside the window? _____

Buford may be a bit of a bully— but
he really does like Baljeet.
Baljeet may be brainy— but he finds
it hard to think around Buford.

Baljeet needs your help.
Buford will not get up until you have located
the pages on which these images occur
throughout this book.

Please hurry!
Thank you so much.

①  PAGE _____   ② PAGE _____

③  PAGE _____   ④ PAGE _____

⑤ PAGE _____   ⑥ PAGE _____

⑦ PAGE _____   ⑧ PAGE _____

SLIME TIME!

Ferb knows how to make everything—even green slime! Do you want to learn how to make slime like Ferb? It's easy!

Please ask an adult or older brother or sister for help before you begin!

What you need:

- 1 cup of cornstarch
- 1/2 cup of water
- Green food coloring (liquid food coloring—not the gel kind.) If you don't have green, you can mix blue and yellow food coloring
- Mixing bowl

Directions:

1. Pour one cup of cornstarch into the bowl.
2. Slowly pour 1/2 cup of water into the bowl.
3. Add a few drops of green food coloring (or a few drops each of blue and yellow)
4. Use your hands to mix the water and cornstarch together.

SLIME RHYME

Look, up, down, across, and diagonally for these words.

E	F	E	R	B	E	E
E	N	E	M	I	M	M
M	M	Z	E	I	I	I
I	E	M	Y	H	R	H	L	D
T	L	I	M	E	M	I	C	C
S	P	R	I	M	E	

time
nime
crime
rhyme   dime
prime   lime
chime   slime
climb   enzyme

Where's Perry?

Perry the Platypus is part mindless domestic pet...

How many words with **4 or more letters** can you make from the letters in:

PERRY THE PLATYPUS

_____   _____

_____   _____

_____   _____

_____   _____

_____   _____

_____   _____

_____   _____

_____   _____

_____   _____

_____   _____

...and part secret agent—trying to save the tri-state area from the very evil Dr. Heinz Doofenshmirtz!

SEMI-AQUATIC, EGG-LAYIN' MAMMAL OF ACTION

When called to duty, Perry slips off to his lair and becomes Agent P. Major Monogram briefs Agent P on Dr. Doofenshmirtz's evil schemes.

SECRET DECODER

SECRET CODE

Dr. Doofenshmirtz is nowhere to be found! Agent P's superior officer, Major Monogram, gives Agent P two possible reasons for his mysterious disappearance—but they're in code! What do they say?

REASON 1

___ ___ ___ ___ ___   ___ ___ ___ ___ ___   ___ ___ ___ ___ ___ ___ ___ ___ ___ ___ ___
13   1   7   9   3   5   12   22   5   19   20   18   1   14   19   16   15   18   20   5   4

___ ___ ___   ___ ___   ___ ___   ___ ___ ___ ___ ___   ___ ___ ___ ___   ___ ___ ___ ___ .
8   9   13   20   15   1   14   1   14   7   18   25   3   15   18   14   12   1   14   4

REASON 2

, ___ ___   ___   ___ ___ ___ ___ ___ ___   ___ ___   ___ ___   ___ ___ ___ ___ ___ ___
8   5   19   8   9   4   9   14   7   15   14   1   14   9   19   12   1   14   4

___ ___ ___ ___   ___   ___ ___ ___ ___ ___   ___   ___ ___   ___ ___ .
23   9   20   8   1   7   9   1   14   20   4   15   14   9   20

Dalmatian Press

STRING OF SPIKES

Phineas and Ferb want to create a quick escape mechanism from their tree house to the roof of their garage. They try a rope—but it's just too slick! Ferb quietly fills two trashcans with water— and a strange white powder. What could he be up to?

Result Timing: 2 days

Find out what Ferb may be creating.

Please ask an adult or older brother or sister for help before you begin!

What you need:
- Water
- 2 plastic cups
- 12 inches of cotton string
- Baking soda
- Tablespoon

Directions:
1. Fill the plastic cups with water.
2. Measure 1 tablespoon of baking soda into each cup.
3. Put one end of the string in one cup and the other end of the string in the other cup.
4. Let the string and the cups sit for two days. (Do not stir, shake, jiggle, wiggle, or do anything else to the cups while you're waiting!)
5. After 2 days, check your string. What do you see? Draw a picture of what the string looked like before and after your experiment.

Beginning of Day 1

End of Day 2

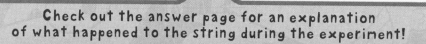

Check out the answer page for an explanation of what happened to the string during the experiment!

Candace needs an extreme tree house makeover.

Design a new and improved tree house for her.

Fun never falls too far from the tree house.

Dalmatian Press

A LITTLE INFLATION

The evil Dr. Doofenshmirtz has a new invention—the Deflate-inator. He aims it at a beach ball in a stadium, and—f-f-f-f-f—it deflates! "I will deflate everything in the tri-state area," he gloats, "forcing everyone to come to me if they want something inflated!"

No need to fear the Deflate-inator. Make your own INFLATE-INATOR!

Please ask an adult or older brother or sister for help before you begin!

What you need:

- **Small water or juice bottle, empty and rinsed out** (The top should be small enough that you can stretch the opening of a balloon over it.)
- **Latex balloon** (roundish, new)
- **4 tablespoons vinegar**
- **2 tablespoons baking soda**
  Optional: a small funnel is helpful for getting the baking soda into the balloon.

Making an Inflate-inator can be a little messy, so set this up near the kitchen sink and have some paper towels handy for clean-up.

Directions:

1. Pour the vinegar into the bottle.
2. Using a piece of paper shaped into a cone (or a small funnel), spoon the baking soda into the balloon.
3. Holding the balloon so that the baking soda doesn't tip into the bottle, stretch the opening of the balloon to fit over the neck of the bottle.
4. Slowly straighten out the balloon and tip it upside down so that the baking soda falls into the vinegar in the bottle.

Before

What happens? Draw pictures of the balloon and bottle as they looked before the experiment and after the experiment.

Check out the answer page for an explanation of what happened.

After

NAME YOUR NEMESIS!

Grab a nemesis (or just a good friend) and challenge him or her to a game!

TIC-TAC-TOE

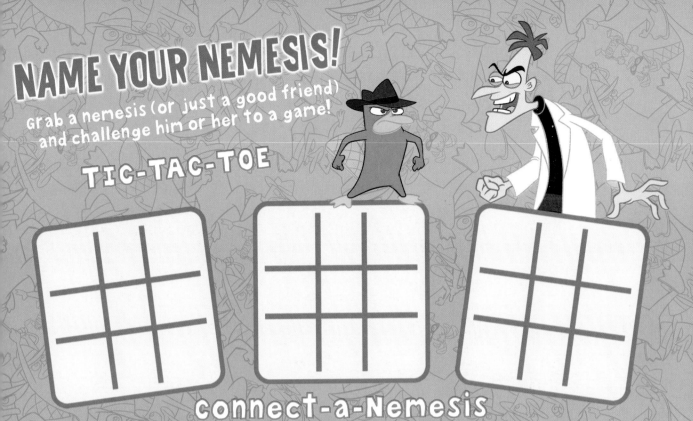

Connect-a-Nemesis

Player #1 draws a line to connect two dots. (You can draw up and down, or across, but not diagonally.) Then Player #2 connects two dots. At some point, a player will connect two dots that will complete a square! Yay! That player puts his initials inside the square and gets a point. Squares with a trashcan are worth 2 points. When all the dots are connected, the game is over. The player with the most points is the winner!

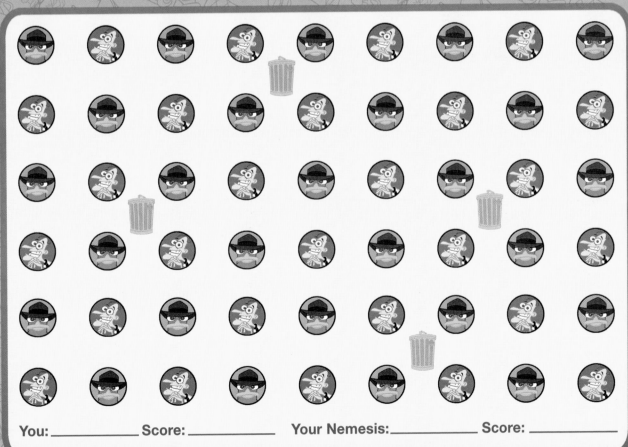

You: _____ Score: _____   Your Nemesis: _____ Score: _____

Dalmatian Press

GAME ON!

You can play fun games just by looking at the things around you! First, can you find some things around you that match the colors in these boxes? Write them down! Then, look around to see if you can spot items that begin with the letters in the boxes and write those down, too!

A	D	F	P
W	L	H	M
S	N	C	G
T	B	J	R

How long did it take you?_____

Fill-in Fun!

Phineas and Ferb are camping at their grandparents' lake—and what a day they've had! But words are missing from their story—and you can fix that! First, fill in the purple list of needed words. (Have friends make lists on separate sheets of paper.) Then, inserting the words from your list, read your awesome retelling of the gang's day searching for Badbeard's treasure!

friend #1 name	1. _____
musical instrument	2. _____
friend #2 name	3. _____
animal	4. _____
friend #3 name	5. _____
article of clothing	6. _____
number	7. _____
adjective	8. _____
foreign country	9. _____
body part	10. _____
adjective	11. _____
body part (plural)	12. _____
adjective	13. _____
a reptile	14. _____
something gross	15. _____
adjective	16. _____
adjective	17. _____
noun (plural)	18. _____

"Toot-toot!" Phineas and Ferb woke up at camp to a strange sound. "Must be ___(1)___ playing a(n) ___(2)___," Phineas said. "Sounds like ___(3)___ strangling a(n) ___(4)___!" They left their tent and noticed that ___(5)___'s ___(6)___ was waving from the flagpole.

"Cool!" Phineas exclaimed.

The boys and their ___(7)___ friends went to Badbeard's Lake, named for captain Badbeard, a(n) ___(8)___ pirate from ___(9)___. "Badbeard hid his treasure on Spleen Island," Grandpa explained. He pulled a map from his ___(10)___ and read: "whoever dares to open the treasure chest will be cursed with ___(11)___ ___(12)___ forever!"

"Cool!" Phineas cheered.

Ferb helped the kids build a ___(13)___ ship, and they sailed off toward the island. They were chased by a giant ___(14)___ all the way to ___(15)___ Cave! There they found Badbeard's treasure chest! It was full of ___(16)___, ___(17)___, tacky ___(18)___!

BY GEORGE, I THINK B'S GOT IT!

Dr. Heinz Doofenshmirtz is up to his nasty tricks again—plotting to take over the world (or at least the tri-state area).

"The tri-state area is filled with so many things I detest—like blinking traffic arrows! Ear hair! And pelicans—terrible creatures! Ugh—musical instruments that start with the letter B. I have built something that will make these awful things disappear. Behold, Perry the Platypus... my Shrink Spheria! Its rays turn all particles into sparticles, thereby shrinking it into a teeny, tiny speck!"

OBJECT HUNT

Uh, oh. . . Dr. Doofenshmirtz's Shrink Spheria went wacky and started to shrink ALL objects that start with the letter B! Agent P must find and hide them all! Look through this whole book and list all the things you spot that start with B. How many can you find?

As the dastardly Dr. Doofenshmirtz plots, Agent P is trapped by George Washington and Abraham Lincoln (they're really just robotic wax statues from a wax museum that was going out of business).

WORD FIND

Can you find these words that describe moves Agent P might make to free himself from Abe and George? Look up, down, across, and diagonally.

LUNGE
JUMP
LEAP
BAM
SLAP
SLAM
BOP
STRIKE
CHOP
PIN
HIT
JAB

S	O	L	J	T	B	P
Y	L	E	U	A	I	O
S	L	A	M	N	B	H
B	O	P	P	A	G	C
D	S	T	R	I	K	E

AGENT P TO THE RESCUE!

Which shadow of Agent P is an exact match to the image at the right?

A

B

C

D

SAVING THE WORLD FROM MANIACAL EVIL ONE DAY AT A TIME!

MEAP ME AT THE SPACE STATION

Which line leads the remote-control baseball to Meap's spacecraft?

OOPS! Phineas and Ferb accidentally knocked an alien into their backyard with one of their remote-control baseballs. He's a cute little fellow! Candace thinks so, too. She whisks him off to a Bango-Ru convention in the basket of her bicycle—while her brothers repair Meap's spacecraft. They all end up in the space station of Meap's nemesis—Mitch! Dr. Doofenshmirtz's latest invention causes all the balloons in the tri-state area to also gather at the space station—making for a typical fun-filled gathering on an ordinary summer afternoon for Phineas and Ferb.

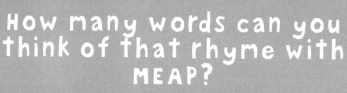

How many words can you think of that rhyme with MEAP?

_____   _____

_____   _____

_____   _____

_____   _____

_____   _____

_____   _____

_____   _____

_____   _____

There are two maze paths that lead from the space station—one to Candace and Meap, and the other to Phineas, Ferb, and Isabella. Can you find them?

START

Finish

Finish

Study these sections—then find and circle the exact areas they came from in the balloon picture.

A

B

C

Whatcha do-hic!

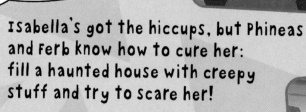

Isabella's got the hiccups, but Phineas and Ferb know how to cure her: fill a haunted house with creepy stuff and try to scare her!

There's only one exact mirror image of the monsters. Can you find it?

A

C

B

Use the grid to draw Candace and her hair-raising experience in the haunted house.

ANSWERS

Page 2

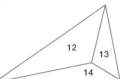
1 overall, 2, 3, 10, 8, 4, 5, 6, 11, 9, 7

Did you find more than 16? Good job!
15, 16, 19, 17, 18

More than 23? Brilliant!
24, 25

28, 27

12, 13, 14

20, 21, 23, 22

If you found 28, you're as smart as Ferb!
26

Page 2

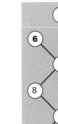
2, 6, 3, 7, 8, 5, 9, 4, 1

Page 3

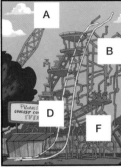
A, B, D, F

Page 3

Snake tail on back car, sunglasses off boy, boy with blue shirt, and purple snake.

Clouds and building missing and no inner area on wheels

Page 4

Page 5

1. **FLYNN**
2. **FLETCHER**
3. **RUSHMORE**
4. **PLATYPUS**
5. **VANESSA**
6. **SPACE**
7. **HEINZ**
8. **CRAYON**
9. **SUMMER**

Page 6

1. T
2. T
3. F
4. T
5. T
6. T
7. F
8. T
9. T
10. F
11. T
12. T

Page 7

KUSNK — SKUNK
MALLA — LLAMA
ANAIGU — IGUANA
DIPSER — SPIDER
FREETR — FERRET
ROONCCA — RACCOON

Page 8

1. There is no shower curtain.
2. One
3. A round life-preserver
4. Bamboo
5. There is no water in the sink.
6. A volcano

Page 8

1. pg 4
2. pg 12
3. pg 19
4. pg 11
5. pg 22
6. pg 5
7. pg 3
8. pg 18

Page 6

M O L E
O
D U C K
S I
N E W T
T O A D
E E
S N A K E
R

A newt is an amphibious animal similar to a salamander.

Page 9

E F E R B E E
E N E M I M M
M M Z E I I I I
I E M Y H R H L D
T L I M E M I C C
S P R I M E

ANSWERS

Page 10

Possible answers (there are more): rate, late, hate, slate, plate, trap, type, tape, hurry, tale, pale, sale, these, please, test, rest, play, tray, pray, rash, trash, lash, tasty, pastry

Page 11

REASON 1
MAGIC ELVES TRANSPORTED HIM TO AN ANGRY CORN LAND.

REASON 2
HE'S HIDING ON AN ISLAND WITH A GIANT D ON IT.

Page 12

STRING OF SPIKES EXPLANATION
The water is attracted to the string because the string is drier than the water. It moves into the string through a process called osmosis. It brings the baking soda with it, gradually soaking higher up the string. The baking soda collects on the string and forms small clumps or spikes.

Page 14

A LITTLE INFLATION EXPLANATION
When you mix substances like vinegar and baking soda, you cause a chemical reaction to happen. The chemical reaction changes the original ingredients in some way. In this case, vinegar and baking soda "react" to each other and produce bubbles of carbon dioxide, an invisible gas. The carbon dioxide rises into the air where it's caught in the balloon and partially inflates it.

Page 18

OBJECTS THAT START WITH THE LETTER B
Possible answers (there are more): back yard, Buford, bowl, bamboo, blowtorch, boot, banana peel, baking soda, balloons, bingo board, beards, banjo, bagpipes, bongos, baseball, bike, bathtub, Baljeet, bottle, boy, belt, board, bolt, bulb, buildings, blueprint, bark, beam, bubble, bumper, box, brush, basin, brothers, bathmat

Page 19

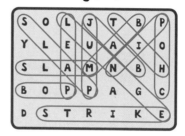

Page 19

Page 20

Page 20

Possible answers: beep, cheap, cheep, creep, deep, heap, keep, leap, peep, seep, sheep, sleep, steep, sweep, weep, asleep

Page 21

Page 21

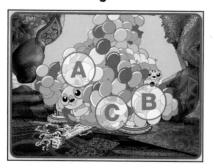

Page 22